THE GREAT BIBLE DISCOVERY

EZEKIEL AND ISAIAH

THE BIBLE IS A BEST-SELLER. IT IS ALSO ONE OF THE MASTER-WORKS OF WORLD LITERATURE - SO IMPORTANT THAT UNIVERSITIES TODAY TEACH 'NON-RELIGIOUS' BIBLE COURSES TO HELP STUDENTS WHO CHOOSE TO STUDY WESTERN LITERATURE.

THE BIBLE POSSESSES AN AMAZING POWER TO FASCINATE YOUNG AND OLD ALIKE.

ONE REASON FOR THIS UNIVERSAL APPEAL IS THAT IT DEALS WITH BASIC HUMAN LONGINGS, EMOTIONS, RELATIONSHIPS. 'ALL THE WORLD IS HERE.' ANOTHER REASON IS THAT SO MUCH OF THE BIBLE CONSISTS OF STORIES. THEY ARE FULL OF MEANING BUT EASY TO REMEMBER.

HERE ARE THOSE STORIES, PRESENTED SIMPLY AND WITH A MINIMUM OF EXPLANATION. WE HAVE LEFT THE TEXT TO SPEAK FOR ITSELF. GIFTED ARTISTS USE THE ACTION-STRIP TECHNIQUE TO BRING THE BIBLE'S DEEP MESSAGE TO READERS OF ALL AGES. THEIR DRAWINGS ARE BASED ON INFORMATION FROM ARCHAEOLOGICAL DISCOVERIES COVERING FIFTEEN CENTURIES.

AN ANCIENT BOOK - PRESENTED FOR THE PEOPLE OF THE SECOND MILLENNIUM. A RELIGIOUS BOOK - PRESENTED FREE FROM THE INTERPRETATION OF ANY PARTICULAR CHURCH. A UNIVERSAL BOOK - PRESENTED IN A FORM THAT ALL MAY ENJOY.

OM publishing
CARLISLE, UK

14

The fall of Jerusalem will have shattered the faith of many Hebrews. Some had believed the false prophets when they said that the Lord would never allow the city of David, with its holy temple, to be destroyed. Now these prophets had been proved wrong. The people of Judah were scattered far and wide. Whom could one believe? Was it the case, perhaps, that the gods of the other nations had showed themselves more powerful? Others had come to understand that the sins of Judah were so great that disaster must come. Now they saw judgment taking place and wondered whether God had rejected his people for ever. Ezekiel behaved in all sorts of strange ways in order to put across his message that there would be no last-minute deliverance for Jerusalem. But he also insisted that there was hope for all who would repent. Today Judah seemed as lifeless as a heap of bones. One day God would give the nation new life.

The words we read in Isaiah 40-55 also contain a mixture of warning and encouragement for the Jews who had been deported to Babylon. Some were tempted to worship the gods of Babylon. Many had given up hope. They had forgotten how, in the days of Ahaz and Hezekiah, the prophet Isaiah had taught that the Lord was in control of all history and of all nations. Now in Babylon they were reminded of this and learned that God had anointed a king who would save them from Babylon. He was a Persian called Cyrus and he captured Babylon and allowed any Jews who wished to return to Jerusalem.

The prophecies in Isaiah 40-55 are so exactly suited to the needs of the exiles that many people have come to think that they were given by God to a prophet living in Babylon at the time. But they certainly form part of the Book of Isaiah and they contain many links with Isaiah 1-39. Did an otherwise unknown prophet of the exile model himself on Isaiah? Or did God guide Isaiah himself to speak words which could be understood by nobody for over a century?

These are questions. What is certain is that Isaiah 40-55 contain some of the most powerful words ever spoken by any prophet.

EZEKIEL

ISAIAH 40-55

EZEKIEL AND ISAIAH

First published as *Découvrir la Bible* 1983

First edition © Larousse S.A. 1984
24-volume series adaptation by Mike Jacklin © Knowledge Unlimited 1994
This edition © OM Publishing 1995

01 00 99 98 97 96 95   7 6 5 4 3 2 1

OM Publishing is an imprint of Send the Light Ltd.,
P.O. Box 300, Carlisle, Cumbria CA3 0QS, U.K.

All rights reserved.
No part of this publication may be reproduced, stored in a retrieval system, or transmitted, in any form or by any means, electronic, mechanical, photocopying, recording or otherwise, without the prior permission of the publishers.

Introductions: Peter Cousins

British Library Cataloguing in Publication Data
A catalogue record for this book is available from the British Library
ISBN 1-85078-218-0

Printed in Singapore by Tien Wah Press (Pte) Ltd.

IN THE LIFE OF EZEKIEL THERE IS A GOOD DEAL ABOUT WHICH WE CANNOT BE SURE.
HE WAS CALLED TO BE A PROPHET IN 593 OR 592 BC, AND HE CONTINUED TO PREACH GOD'S WORD UNTIL HE DIED IN 573. WAS HE ONE OF THE PEOPLE NEBUCHADNEZZAR II DEPORTED FROM JERUSALEM IN 597, SO THAT HIS WHOLE MINISTRY WAS ONLY IN BABYLON? OR DID HE PROPHESY FIRST IN JERUSALEM, BEFORE BEING SENT TO BABYLON IN 587, WHERE HE PREACHED TO HIS BROTHERS IN EXILE?

EZEKIEL
A prophet deported to Babylon

IN THE SIXTH YEAR OF THE REIGN OF KING **ZEDEKIAH** THE WORD OF THE LORD CAME TO ME, **EZEKIEL**, SON OF THE PRIEST BUZI, AND GOD'S HAND WAS ON ME...

HE SAID TO ME, 'MAN, I'M SENDING YOU TO THE ISRAELITES WHO HAVE REBELLED AGAINST ME, BUT WHETHER OR NOT THEY LISTEN TO YOU, THEY'LL KNOW THAT THERE'S A PROPHET AMONG THEM...'

SCENARIO: Etienne DAHLER
DRAWING: Carlo MARCELLO

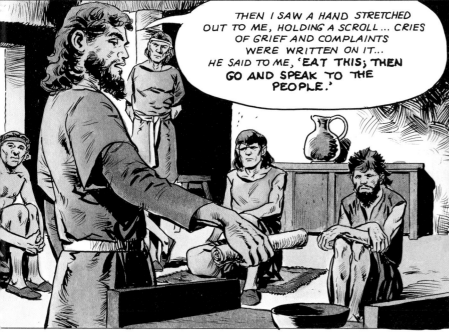

THEN I SAW A HAND STRETCHED OUT TO ME, HOLDING A SCROLL... CRIES OF GRIEF AND COMPLAINTS WERE WRITTEN ON IT... HE SAID TO ME, 'EAT THIS; THEN GO AND SPEAK TO THE PEOPLE.'

I ATE IT, AND IT WAS AS SWEET AS HONEY IN MY MOUTH.

MASTER, WHAT DID YOU REPLY?

NOTHING! WHEN GOD SPEAKS, THERE'S NOTHING TO BE SAID!

A PROPHET? RUBBISH! YOUR MASTER IS NOTHING BUT A STORY-TELLER! YOU'RE WASTING YOUR TIME WITH HIM!

THE SWORD WILL BE UN-SHEATHED, AND EVERY ONE FROM SOUTH TO NORTH WILL DIE!

THERE'S NO DANGER! TIME PASSES, AND NONE OF THESE VISIONS COMES TRUE!

WHEN THE PROPHET LEFT HIS HOUSE, A PEASANT CALLED OUT TO HIS DISCIPLE.

WHEN HE REACHED THE VILLAGE SQUARE, EZEKIEL STOPPED IN FRONT OF A GROUP OF TRADERS.

I WILL SILENCE THEM, SAYS THE LORD. THE TIME IS NEAR WHEN THESE VISIONS WILL COME TRUE!

THE END IS COMING! THE DAY OF THE LORD IS COMING!

ALL THAT IS OUT OF DATE! KING NEBUCHADNEZZAR WENT BACK TO BABYLON MANY YEARS AGO. WHY SHOULD HE COME BACK TO US HERE?

BUT IN JERUSALEM IN 589 KING ZEDEKIAH REBELLED AGAINST HIS BABYLONIAN OVERLORD.

EGYPT PROMISES TO HELP US. WE'VE ALREADY RECEIVED CHARIOTS AND HORSES.

BUT, KING ZEDEKIAH, WE CAN'T HOLD OUT AGAINST NEBUCHADNEZZAR!

I'VE COME TO A DECISION! THIS YEAR WE WON'T PAY THE TRIBUTE TO BABYLON!

THE NEWS QUICKLY SPREAD THROUGH THE LITTLE KINGDOM OF JUDAH. PREPARATIONS FOR WAR WERE ALREADY WELL IN HAND.

BABYLON MADE A TREATY WITH OUR KING. DO YOU THINK YOU CAN SUCCEED, WHEN YOU BREAK YOUR OATH?

IN THE STREETS OF JERUSALEM EZEKIEL CALLED OUT...

THE LORD SAYS: IT IS MY OATH HE HAS REJECTED, MY TREATY HE HAS BROKEN! I'LL MAKE HIM PAY FOR IT!

JERUSALEM, YOU'VE BEHAVED LIKE A PROSTITUTE; YOU'VE DISGRACED YOUR BEAUTY; YOU'VE GIVEN YOURSELF TO ANYBODY PASSING BY...

EZEKIEL CRITICIZED JERUSALEM, WHICH STOOD FOR THE WHOLE KINGDOM.

...TO THE EGYPTIANS, TO THE ASSYRIANS, TO THE BABYLONIAN MERCHANTS—AND YOU'RE STILL NOT SATISFIED!

LISTEN TO THE LORD! I'LL GATHER ALL YOUR LOVERS TOGETHER, AND DELIVER YOU INTO THEIR HANDS...

...THEY'LL STONE YOU AND RUN YOU THROUGH WITH THEIR SWORDS... THEY'LL PUT AN END TO YOUR TERRIBLE CRIMES.

EZEKIEL IS TALKING LIKE JEREMIAH!

I WONDER WHAT IS IN STORE FOR US.

AND YET THE CITIES OF SODOM AND SAMARIA DIDN'T SIN HALF AS MUCH AS JERUSALEM HAS...

EZEKIEL WENT BACK TO HIS VILLAGE... MORE THAN 1 000 KM AWAY THE BABYLONIAN ARMY WAS ON THE MARCH...

HERE ARE TWO ROADS: ONE GOES TO RABBAT AMMON,* THE OTHER TO JERUSALEM...

*Today, AMMAN, the capital of Jordan.

WHEN HE COMES TO THE FORK IN THE ROAD NEBUCHADNEZZAR HESITATES: WHICH CITY SHOULD HE ATTACK?

IN FACT, AT THAT VERY MOMENT THE KING OF BABYLON WAS HESITATING...

WE MUST ASK THE GODS WHICH ROAD TO TAKE...

YOU MUST TAKE THE ROAD TO THE RIGHT, THE ROAD TO JERUSALEM.

THE DAY OF THE LORD IS NEAR. NEBUCHADNEZZAR IS READY TO ATTACK US!

THEN EZEKIEL WENT HOME. HIS WIFE KEPT QUIET WHILE HE MADE BREAD FROM WHEAT, BARLEY, AND MILLET.

HE HASN'T BEEN SEEN FOR NEARLY A WEEK!

PERHAPS HE'S ILL...

LET'S HOPE HE HASN'T DIED!

WHAT HAS HAPPENED TO HIM?

LOOK! HE HAS MADE A LOAF THAT'S ROTTEN!

EZEKIEL! SAY SOMETHING TO US!

LEAVE HIM... HE'S NO MORE SICK THAN YOU OR I !

I'VE TURNED TO THE NORTH, TO CARRY THE SINS OF ISRAEL*...

* The Northern Kingdom; its people had been deported by the Assyrians in 721 after the fall of Samaria.

AT LAST THE PROPHET GOT UP.

THE TIME FOR BEING SORRY IS OVER! BRING ME MY RAZOR, AND TELL THE ELDERS TO COME HERE AT ONCE.

BUT, EZEKIEL, WHAT ARE YOU DOING?

YOUR HUSBAND HAS GONE MAD!

HERE ARE THE PEOPLE OF JUDAH...

ONE THIRD OF THEM WILL DIE FROM PLAGUE...

ONE THIRD WILL FALL BY THE SWORD...

...AND ONE THIRD WILL BE SCATTERED TO THE WINDS!

BESIEGED BY THE BABYLONIAN ARMY, JERUSALEM HOPED FOR HELP FROM **EGYPT AND TYRE**. BUT GOD SPOKE THROUGH THE PROPHET...

DON'T PUT YOUR HOPE IN EGYPT!

YOU, THE PHARAOH, THE MONSTER CROCODILE! I'LL RUN YOU THROUGH WITH SPEARS. I'LL PULL YOU OUT OF THE NILE, AND THROW YOU INTO THE DESERT. THEN EVERYONE WILL KNOW THAT I'M THE LORD!

IN MARCH 587 BC, EGYPT TRIED TO LIFT THE SIEGE OF JERUSALEM, BUT FAILED.

AS FOR THE CITY OF TYRE...

AS THE WAVES BREAK, I'LL BREAK ALL THE NATIONS OVER YOU.

...THEY'LL DESTROY YOUR WALLS, KNOCK DOWN YOUR TOWERS...

...I'LL SWEEP AWAY THE DUST! I'LL MAKE YOU A BARE ROCK. THIS IS WHAT THE LORD SAYS!

JERUSALEM! NOTHING COULD CHANGE YOU! AND NOW YOU'RE DYING FAR AWAY FROM YOUR GOD!

IN JERUSALEM, AFTER A YEAR OF SIEGE, THE PEOPLE WERE IN DESPAIR... IN HIS PRISON THE PROPHET JEREMIAH WAS BORED TO DEATH.

JERUSALEM DURING THE SIEGE
D'S WORD CAME TO EZEKIEL...

MAN, THIS IS HOW I'M GOING TO
TAKE THE JOY OUT OF YOUR EYES,
BUT YOU MUSTN'T WEEP OR
MOURN.

THAT NIGHT
THE PROPHET'S
WIFE DIED...

THAT SAME NIGHT KING ZEDEKIAH TRIED TO ESCAPE FROM THE BABYLONIANS BY FLEEING FROM JERUSALEM.

COME ON! THE WAY IS CLEAR!

WELL! WELL! THE KING OF JUDAH! RUNNING AWAY WITH HIS WHOLE FAMILY!

HEN HE WAS TAKEN PRISONER AT DAWN,
WAS AS IF KING ZEDEKIAH HAD SIGNED
E HOLY CITY'S DEATH SENTENCE.

EZEKIEL, WE DON'T KNOW WHAT TO SAY... SUCH A SUDDEN DEATH...

AND YOU... NOT A TEAR... AND NOT IN MOURN- ING!

THIS IS WHAT THE LORD SAYS: THIS IS HOW I'LL ALLOW MY HOLY PLACE TO BE MADE UNCLEAN, THE TEMPLE WHICH IS MY PRIDE AND JOY.

LORD! LORD! DON'T TEST US SO SEVERELY!

THE PROPHET'S FRIENDS RIPPED THEIR CLOTHES AS A SIGN OF MOURNING, BUT EZEKIEL EXPLAINED THE STRANGE WAY HE WAS BEHAVING.

...SO EZEKIEL WILL BE A SIGN FOR YOU, AND YOU'LL DO WHAT HE HAS DONE.

COME QUICKLY! THERE'S A MAN IN THE VILLAGE SQUARE WHO HAS FLED FROM JERUSALEM!

THE CITY WAS CAPTURED THIS MORNING! BLOOD IS FLOWING EVERYWHERE...

IS ANYONE LEFT ALIVE? AND WHERE'S JEREMIAH?

I DON'T KNOW! I LEFT SO QUICKLY...

KING NEBUCHADNEZZAR LEFT JERUSALEM, SENDING THE IMPORTANT AND STRONG MEN INTO EXILE IN BABYLON. THE CITY WAS IN RUINS. GANGS OF LOOTERS WERE BUSY EVERYWHERE.

THE CITIZENS WHOSE LIVES WERE SPARED BY THE BABYLONIAN SOLDIERS SOUGHT REFUGE IN THE VILLAGES AROUND JERUSALEM.

EZEKIEL WENT TO LIVE WITH THE JERUSALEM EXILES ON THE BANKS OF THE KEBAR CANAL, NEAR TO BABYLON. ONE DAY...

...HE FOUND HIMSELF FACE TO FACE WITH GOD'S GLORY.

MAN, STAND UP, AND LISTEN! GO TO THE EXILES AND TAKE MY WORD TO THEM!

SO THE PROPHET SETTLED AT TEL-ABIB, ONE OF THE VILLAGES WHERE THE EXILES LIVED.

HE HASN'T HAD ANYTHING TO EAT OR DRINK FOR SEVERAL DAYS!

AND HE DOESN'T SEEM TO SEE US ANY MORE.

SUDDENLY A SPRING OF WATER WAS RUNNING OUT UNDER THE ENTRANCE TO THE TEMPLE...

THIS WATER FLOWS DOWN TO THE DEAD SEA, TO MAKE IT FRESH AGAIN.

THESE TREES WILL BEAR FRUIT EVERY MONTH, AND THEIR LEAVES WILL BE USED TO CURE ALL SICKNESSES.

BUT WHEN WILL THIS HAPPEN?

WHAT ARE YOU TALKING ABOUT?

EZEKIEL, YOU THINK ABOUT JERUSALEM TOO MUCH! WE'RE IN BABYLON!

...TER THIS VISION OF A NEW TEMPLE, THE PROPHET ...ED, WITHOUT LEARNING THE ANSWER...

...WHILE TIME WAS EATING AWAY THE RUINS OF JERUSALEM.

I WILL GIVE THEM A NEW HEART, AND I WILL PUT A NEW SPIRIT IN THEM. I WILL TAKE AWAY THEIR STUBBORN, STONY HEART, AND GIVE THEM AN OBEDIENT ONE.

EZEKIEL 11:19

A NEW ISAIAH

IN THE YEAR 570 BC BABYLON WAS THE GREATEST CITY IN THE NEAR EAST.

SCENARIO: Etienne DAHLER
DRAWING: Victor de la FUENTE

BUSINESS HAS NEVER BEEN SO GOOD!

IN BABYLON, IN THE MIDDLE OF THE DESERT, EVERYTHING GROWS!

SOON, IN THE ROYAL PALACE, THE FESTIVAL WAS AT ITS HEIGHT...

WINTER IS OVER! ISHTAR RISES FROM THE UNDERWORLD. ISHTAR IS HONOURED! ISHTAR IS QUEEN. YOUR LOOK BRINGS LIFE TO WHAT WAS DEAD. LOOK AT ME; ACCEPT MY PRAYER!

YOU HEAR THE FLUTES AND THE DRUM ROLLS? THEY SAY THAT SPRING IS HERE!

THEN ISHTAR* APPEARED, PLAYED BY A TEMPLE PROSTITUTE, THE KING'S FAVOURITE.

BLESSED BE THE GODDESS ISHTAR, WHO COMES BACK FROM THE UNDERWORLD!

THAT WOMAN HAS BEWITCHED THE KING... SHE'S INFLUENCED THE KING TO WORSHIP ISHTAR, AND FORGET ABOUT OUR GOD BAAL.

*The Babylonian name for Astarte.

THE KING'S NEW FAVOURITE EVEN MANAGED TO WIN SOME OF THE JEWS IN BABYLON TO HER RELIGION.

MOSHE! I'VE SOMETHING IN GOLD...

TELL ME...

A STATUE OF ISHTAR! EVERYBODY WHO HAS ONE WILL HAVE GOOD LUCK!

STARTING WITH YOU, YOU SLY OLD FELLOW!

MEANWHILE THERE WERE STILL SOME WHO WERE TRUE TO THE TEACHING OF EZEKIEL, THE GREAT PROPHET WHO HAD BEEN DEAD FOR MANY YEARS. ONE OF THEM WAS A YOUNG PROPHET...

THE LORD NEVER ABANDONS HIS PEOPLE!

BUT MANY OF OUR BROTHERS ABANDON HIM!

EVERYTHING DEPENDS ON THOSE WHO REMAIN FAITHFUL. IT HAS ALWAYS BEEN LIKE THAT.

I KNOW... EZEKIEL SAID THAT THE PEOPLE OF ISRAEL WOULD GO BACK TO THEIR LAND. BUT, ISAIAH, HOW AND WHEN IS THAT GOING TO HAPPEN?

OBEY THE LAW. THE LORD WILL DO THE REST.

...BABYLON, A PRISON WITH GOLDEN DOORS!

AT THE GATE OF THE CITY THE YOUNG PROPHET WAS DEEP IN THOUGHT.

LORD, MY GOD, SEND A WORD OF COMFORT TO YOUR PEOPLE... AND TO ME, YOUR SERVANT, AS WELL!

BESIDE THE RIVER SOME YOUNG EXILES WERE WORKING UNDER AN OVERSEER.

YOU ISRAELITE GIRLS, SING US A SONG FROM YOUR HOMELAND.

HOW CAN WE SING IN A FOREIGN LAND? JERUSALEM, IF I EVER FORGET YOU, MAY MY TONGUE CLING TO THE ROOF OF MY MOUTH!

BABYLON, MAY DISASTER COME UPON YOU... MAY THE BOLTS OF OUR PRISON-DOORS FALL OFF!

GRADUALLY THE PEOPLE CAME TO LOOK UP TO THE YOUNG PROPHET...

HE'S ANOTHER ISAIAH, FILLED WITH THE SPIRIT.

SOME ARE EVEN SAYING IT IS ISAIAH COME BACK TO LIFE!

ISRAEL, YOU'RE MY SERVANT. I CHOSE YOU; I HAVEN'T REJECTED YOU.

HERE'S MY SERVANT: HE'LL OPEN THE EYES OF THE BLIND, LET THE CAPTIVES OUT OF PRISON, AND FREE THOSE WHO ARE IN DARKNESS FROM THEIR DUNGEON.

NEBUCHADNEZZAR DIED. HIS SUCCESSOR, **AMEL-MARDUK**, SET FREE JEHOIACHIN, THE KING OF JUDAH, WHO HAD BEEN IN PRISON SINCE HE WAS TAKEN TO BABYLON.*

TAKE YOUR PLACE IN THE ROYAL PALACE, JEHOIACHIN; I'M GIVING YOU YOUR PEOPLE.

See Jeremiah (Vol. 13, pages 40-41).

...BUT BE CAREFUL. AT THE FIRST SIGN OF DISOBEDIENCE I'LL PUT YOU TO DEATH!

A LITTLE WHILE LATER ISAIAH PROPHESIED IN A SYNAGOGUE IN BABYLON.

YOU'LL THRESH THE MOUNTAINS AND CRUSH THEM. YOU'LL CRUMBLE THE HILLS TO CHAFF, AND THE WIND WILL BLOW THEM AWAY.

WHAT DO YOU MEAN? WE'RE NOT GOING TO REBEL AGAINST BABYLON!

I'VE CHOSEN A MAN. HE IS A FOREIGNER, AND HE'LL SET YOU FREE...

MY SON, YOUR WORDS DISTURB ME, AND...

WHAT ARE YOU AFRAID OF? I AM THE FIRST AND THE LAST; THERE IS NO OTHER GOD BUT ME, SAYS THE LORD, THE KING OF ISRAEL.

BUT AT THE COURT OF BABYLON NOBODY WAS TAKING MUCH NOTICE OF THE JEWS AND THEIR PROPHETS.
A PALACE REVOLUTION HAD BROUGHT *A STRANGE PERSON TO POWER: NABONIDUS, SON OF A PRIESTESS OF SIN,* AND ONE OF HIS FAITHFUL WORSHIPPERS. *THE MOON GOD

MY FRIEND, I'M VERY ANXIOUS.

KING NABONIDUS, THE RISE OF CYRUS TO POWER IN PERSIA IS VERY WORRYING...

IT ISN'T THAT! SIN AND MARDUK HAVE ORDERED ME TO STOP THE OTHER GODS FROM BEING ANGRY BY DECORATING THEIR TEMPLES.

BUT, YOUR MAJESTY...

THE IDOLS THE BABYLONIANS LOVE SO MUCH ARE GOOD FOR NOTHING! ONE DAY THEY'LL BE ASHAMED OF THEM.

SOON AFTERWARDS KING NABONIDUS LEFT BABYLON TO VISIT AND DECORATE THE VERY OLD CITIES OF UR, URUK, AND LARSA... WHILE ISAIAH...

KING NABONIDUS DIDN'T STOP THERE...

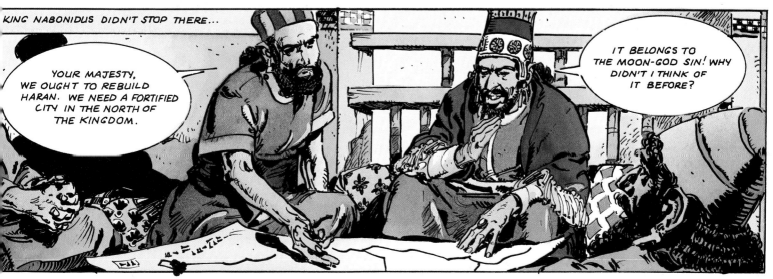

YOUR MAJESTY, WE OUGHT TO REBUILD HARAN. WE NEED A FORTIFIED CITY IN THE NORTH OF THE KINGDOM.

IT BELONGS TO THE MOON-GOD SIN! WHY DIDN'T I THINK OF IT BEFORE?

THE KING WILL BE SATISFIED. THIS IS GOING TO BE A BEAUTIFUL CITY.

AND FROM HERE WE'LL CONTROL THE ROADS TO THE NORTH AND THE NORTH-WEST.

NABONIDUS WENT TO DEDICATE THE TEMPLE OF SIN ...

YOU ARE MY GOD!

... WHICH GREATLY UPSET THE BABYLONIAN PRIESTS ...

THE KING IS MAD! SOON SIN WILL BE MORE IMPORTANT THAN MARDUK!

AS FOR ISAIAH...

THE STUPID MAN SHAPES A GOD FROM A PIECE OF WOOD, AND KNEELS AT ITS FEET! DON'T DO THE SAME, ISRAEL!

AS YOU CAN SEE, ISAIAH, SINCE WE'VE BEEN LEFT IN PEACE, THINGS ARE GOING WELL.

GOD IS BLESSING YOU... BUT DON'T FORGET...

THE PROPHET ISAIAH'S FAME SPREAD AMONG THE EXILES. THEY WELCOMED HIM IN NIPPUR, TEL-ABIB, TEL-MELAH...

...THIS ISN'T OUR COUNTRY. THE DAY CAME WHEN ABRAHAM HIMSELF HAD TO LEAVE IT.

DO YOU REALLY BELIEVE THAT WE'LL BE ABLE TO GO BACK TO JUDAH?

I'M SURE OF IT! FROM NOW ON WE MUST BE GETTING READY.

HERE'S OUR VILLAGE. EVERYONE IS WAITING IMPATIENTLY.

SHALOM! PEACE BE WITH YOU!

MAY THE LORD VISIT YOU AND SHOWER YOU WITH GOOD THINGS

IN THIS WAY VILLAGE AFTER VILLAGE TURNED BACK TO GOD. THIS BROUGHT NEW HOPE TO THE EXILES, WHILE IN BABYLON DEVOUT SCRIBES MADE FRESH COPIES OF THE SCRIPTURES AND WROTE NEW ONES.

SOON WHAT ISAIAH HAD BEEN SPEAKING ABOUT, BEGAN TO HAPPEN.

CYRUS, KING OF PERSIA, HAS JUST DEFEATED THE MEDES AND SEIZED THEIR COUNTRY.

MEANWHILE OUR KING NABONIDUS HAS GONE OFF TO CONQUER ARABIA!

IN FACT, WHILE CYRUS WAS MARCHING TOWARDS LYDIA, THE ARMY OF NABONIDUS WAS THRUSTING DEEP INTO THE DESERT...

...AND ARRIVED AT THE OASIS OF TEMA.

KING NABONIDUS, THE GOD SIN HAS SPOKEN. HE GIVES YOU THIS PLACE! YOU MUST RULE FROM HERE!

GREAT NABONIDUS, NO ONE IS MORE SPLENDID THAN YOU!

YOUR PALACE WILL BE THE PEARL OF THE EAST.

NABONIDUS WAS SO HAPPY WITH THIS NEW PLACE THAT HE STAYED THERE 10 YEARS!

MEANWHILE, IN BABYLON, HIS SON BELSHAZZAR ACTED AS REGENT.

THINGS ARE GOING FROM BAD TO WORSE!

TO KEEP THE PERSIANS AWAY, CROESUS, KING OF LYDIA, MADE AN ALLIANCE WITH EGYPT, BUT CYRUS, THE PERSIAN KING, QUICKLY CROSSED THE RIVER HALYS, THE FRONTIER...

...AND WON TWO GREAT VICTORIES.

SHUT UP IN HIS CAPITAL, SARDIS, CROESUS HAD TO SURRENDER AFTER A SIEGE OF 14 DAYS.

CYRUS, EVERYTHING I HAVE IS NOW YOURS!

CROESUS, ACCEPT YOUR SUR- RENDER; YOUR LIFE WILL BE SPARED.

IN BABYLON THE NEW ISAIAH WAS STILL PROPHESYING...

THE LORD SAYS: CYRUS IS MY SHEPHERD. I'VE TAKEN HIM BY HIS RIGHT HAND, TO BRING THE NATIONS UNDER HIS CONTROL, AND PUT THEIR KINGS TO FLIGHT!

I'VE INSPIRED HIM TO PUT THINGS RIGHT. HE'LL REBUILD MY CITY, AND SET MY CAPTIVE PEOPLE FREE. THIS IS THE WORD OF THE LORD.

A FEW DAYS LATER, ISAIAH WAS SPEAKING IN A SYNAGOGUE IN BABYLON...

LOOK OUT! HERE'S PRINCE JEHOIACHIN'S GUARD!

ISAIAH WAS TAKEN TO THE PALACE OF JEHOIACHIN, PRINCE OF JUDAH...

COME HERE, PROPHET! I'D RATHER STOP YOU BEFORE BELSHAZZAR DOES!

YOU TALK ABOUT A MESSIAH! YOU GO SO FAR AS TO SAY...

THAT IT IS CYRUS? YES!

HE'S MAD!

SILENCE HIM!

NEVER SPEAK THAT NAME AGAIN! THE PEOPLE OF JUDAH ARE HAPPY IN BABYLON!

THE LORD DECLARES WHAT IS RIGHT, AND ANNOUNCES WHAT IS TRUE!

TAKE HIM AWAY!

WHEN HE GOT HOME, HIS FRIENDS CAME TO SEE ISAIAH.

I BARED MY BACK TO THOSE WHO BEAT ME. I OFFERED MY CHEEKS TO THOSE WHO PULLED OUT MY BEARD. I DIDN'T TURN AWAY FROM THOSE WHO COVERED ME WITH CURSES.

THE LORD GOD IS MY HELPER; I KNOW I'LL NOT BE PUT TO SHAME.

ISAIAH, THE WAY YOU LIVE TEACHES US MORE THAN WHAT YOU SAY.

NOW WE KNOW THAT ISRAEL WILL BE SAVED THROUGH THE SUFFERING OF ITS SERVANT.

ISAIAH'S WORDS TOUCHED ZERUBBABEL, ONE OF JEHOIACHIN'S IMPORTANT OFFICIALS.

I'M VERY UPSET BY THIS MAN'S WORDS. I'M HAVING SLEEPLESS NIGHTS BECAUSE OF THEM.

NONSENSE! IF YOU WANT MY OPINION, ZERUBBABEL, HE'S NOT WORTH THE BOTHER!

BUT HE'S RIGHT WHEN HE SAYS THAT WE'RE A SPECIAL PEOPLE... AND THAT ALL THE NATIONS WILL COME TO JERUSALEM, AND SEE THE LORD'S SALVATION.

HA! HA! HA! CYRUS WANTS TO ATTACK THE MIGHTY BABYLON!

IN HIS PALACE BELSHAZZAR DIDN'T STOP FEASTING...

COME HERE! STAND UP! LOOK AT THE CITY NO ONE CAN CAPTURE, THE HIGH PLACE OF THE GOD SIN!

YOU SEE THESE STRONG WALLS THAT TOUCH THE SKY? THEY'RE SO WIDE THAT FOUR YOKE OF OXEN CAN WALK ALONG THEM SIDE BY SIDE!

I'LL COVER THE CANALS WITH BRICKS; THEY'LL CAVE IN WHEN CYRUS ATTACKS.

A FEW WEEKS LATER...

KING NABONIDUS HAS COME BACK TO BABYLON. HE'S AFRAID THE CITY WILL BE CAPTURED...

WE'VE CROSSED THE TIGRIS! NOW LET'S MARCH ON THE BABYLONIAN CITIES.

YRUS THE PERSIAN
ONTINUED HIS MARCH
N BABYLON...

IN THE BABYLONIAN CAMP EVERYTHING WAS DONE TO FRIGHTEN THE ENEMY AWAY... BELSHAZZAR'S ARMY PREPARED TO FIGHT.

THE PERSIAN CAVALRYMEN WERE VERY BRAVE. THEY CHARGED BETWEEN THE CHARIOTS AND KILLED THE BABYLONIAN PRINCES.

BABYLON AND THE OTHER CITIES OF THE KINGDOM STILL HELD OUT...

BUT THE TOWN OF **OPIS**, NEAR BABYLON, REBELLED, AND WANTED TO SURRENDER TO CYRUS. NABONIDUS HAD ALL ITS PEOPLE KILLED.

DEATH!

NO MERCY FOR TRAITORS!

THAT DIDN'T STOP MANY FROM JOINING THE PERSIANS... SO THE GOVERNOR OF GUTIUM CAME TO THE GREAT KING CYRUS...

I'M GOBRYAS. I'VE COME TO JOIN YOU.

YOU'RE DOING THE RIGHT THING, BECAUSE I BREAK CHAINS WHEREVER I GO...

BUT WHEN THEY REACHED THE FOOT OF BABYLON'S WALLS, THE SOLDIERS OF CYRUS...

BABYLON, CITY OF THE GODS!

WOE BETIDE US!

WE'RE LOST!

THEY MOVE! I SAW THEM MOVING!

THE SKY IS RUNNING AWAY!

THESE POOR BARBARIANS ARE AFRAID OF THE IDOLS.

THE ARMY OF CYRUS WAS PANIC-STRICKEN... CAMBYSES, HIS SON, WAS WORRIED...

WEEKS WENT BY, AND BABYLON HADN'T YET BEEN TAKEN. CYRUS DISCUSSED IT WITH CAMBYSES.

KING CYRUS, WE HAVE MANY FRIENDS INSIDE THE CITY, BUT, BEFORE THEY CAN HELP US, WE HAVE TO WAIT FOR CIVIL WAR TO BREAK OUT.

NO! LET'S TURN THE EUPHRATES INTO ANOTHER CHANNEL, AND ENTER THE CITY ALONG THE DRY CANALS.

YES, FATHER. I'LL TAKE YOUR ORDERS TO THE ARMY THAT IS BESIEGING THE NORTHERN SIDE.

AT THE SAME TIME, THE PRIESTS INSIDE THE CITY WERE STIRRING UP A REBELLION.

CYRUS WILL MAKE US THE CHIEF PRIESTS AGAIN!

SIN AND ISHTAR HAVE RULED LONG ENOUGH!

LET'S OPEN THE CITY-GATES!

ABYLON WAS CAPTURED WITHOUT ANY LOSS
F LIFE. KING NABONIDUS WAS SPARED,
UT BELSHAZZAR WAS ASSASSINATED.*

       * See Vol. 15, page 16.

LONG LIVE CYRUS, OUR LIBERATOR!

AND IN THE MONTH OF MARCHESHVAN *539, CYRUS MADE HIS ENTRY INTO BABYLON.

LONG LIVE CYRUS!

LONG LIVE THE KING OF BABYLON!

THERE'S THE ONE MARDUK HAS CHOSEN!

    * October - November.

47

THE NEXT YEAR, CYRUS...

THE GOD OF HEAVEN HAS ORDERED ME TO REBUILD HIS TEMPLE IN JERUSALEM. EVERYONE WHO BELONGS TO HIM CAN GO TO JUDAH TO REBUILD THE LORD'S HOUSE THERE.

SO ISAIAH...

YOU WON'T HAVE TO LEAVE BABYLON IN A HURRY; YOU WON'T BE TRYING TO ESCAPE, BECAUSE THE LORD WILL MARCH WITH YOU.

JERUSALEM, CITY OF GOD, I WILL SET YOUR FOUNDATIONS ON PRECIOUS STONES; I WILL MAKE YOUR BATTLEMENTS OUT OF RUBIES, YOUR GATES OF GARNET. THIS IS THE WORD OF THE LORD.

BUT THIS IS WHAT I SEE:
AFTER MANY DAYS, AND BETTER THAN CYRUS,
THE PERFECT SERVANT OF THE LORD.
BY HIS SUFFERINGS, HIS DEATH, AND HIS VICTORY,
HE WILL SET THE MULTITUDES FREE FOR EVER...

The Book of Isaiah.